This
Treasure Cove Story
belongs to

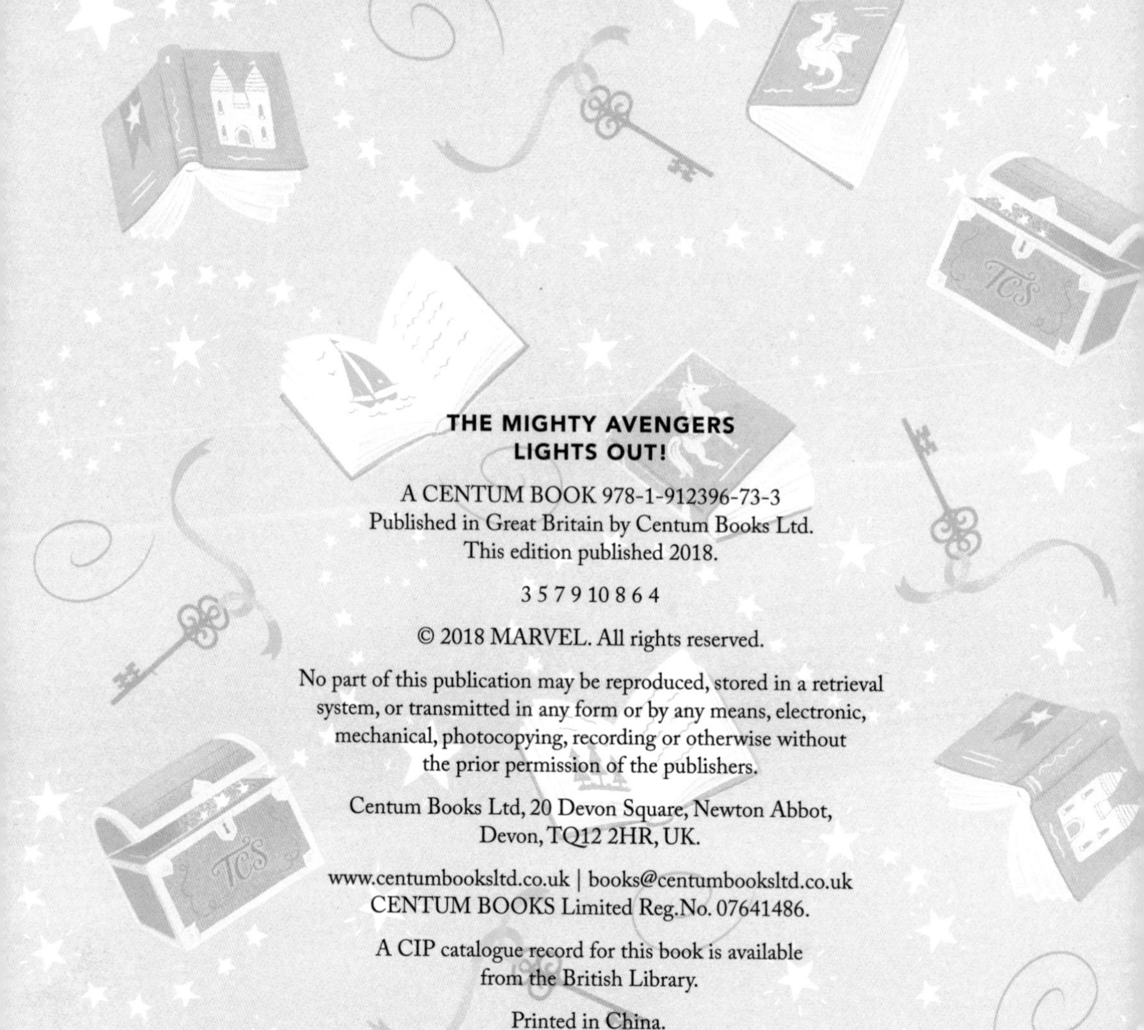

THE MIGHTY AVENGERS
LIGHTS OUT!

A CENTUM BOOK 978-1-912396-73-3
Published in Great Britain by Centum Books Ltd.
This edition published 2018.

3 5 7 9 10 8 6 4

Centum Books Ltd, 20 Devon Square, Newton Abbot, Devon, TQ12 2HR, UK.

www.centumbooksltd.co.uk | books@centumbooksltd.co.uk
CENTUM BOOKS Limited Reg.No. 07641486.

A CIP catalogue record for this book is available from the British Library.

Printed in China.

centum

FSC
www.fsc.org
MIX
Paper from responsible sources
FSC® C149078

A Treasure Cove Story

Based on stories by Marvel Comics
By Courtney Carbone
Illustrated by Patrick Spaziante

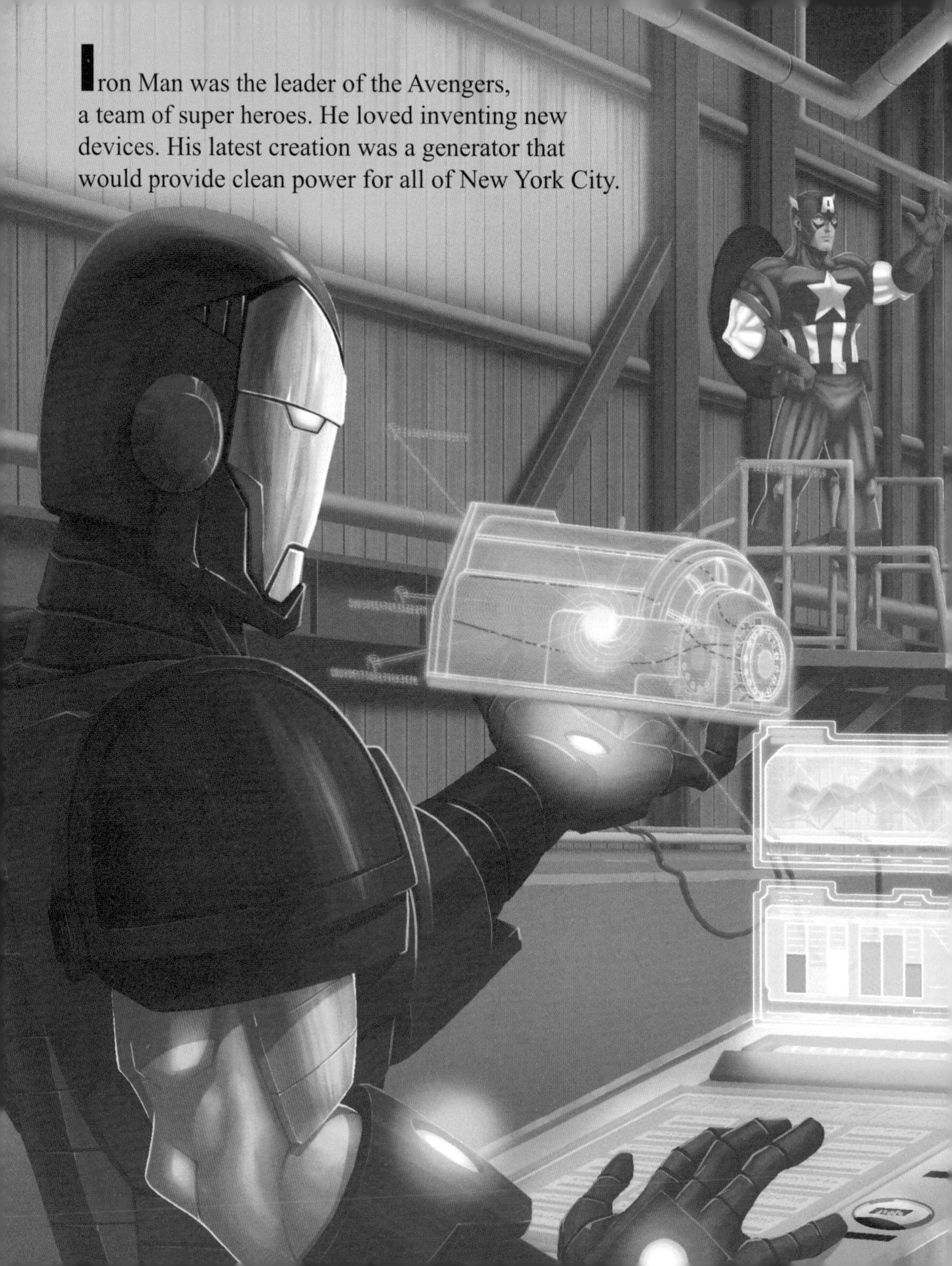

Iron Man was the leader of the Avengers, a team of super heroes. He loved inventing new devices. His latest creation was a generator that would provide clean power for all of New York City.

Captain America, Thor and the Incredible Hulk were helping him install the new generator.

'Careful!' said Iron Man. 'It has one hundred times the power of the old generator.'

WARNING
ENERGY SPIKE DETECTED
ENERGY SPIKE DETECTED

But it was too late: **BOOM!** The generator exploded! The energy crackled and took on the form of a giant glowing monster.

'Zzzax lives again!' the creature roared. 'Zzzax hungers for more power!'

'Energy monster is Hulk's enemy,' Hulk growled. 'Hulk SMASH!'

Zzzax unleashed an energy bolt that sent the green giant crashing through a wall.

'City has power!' Zzzax rumbled. He made his way towards the glowing lights of New York.

Zzzax stomped into the middle of Times Square. 'Power will be mine!' he boomed. Zzzax grew bigger and stronger as he drained energy from the city!

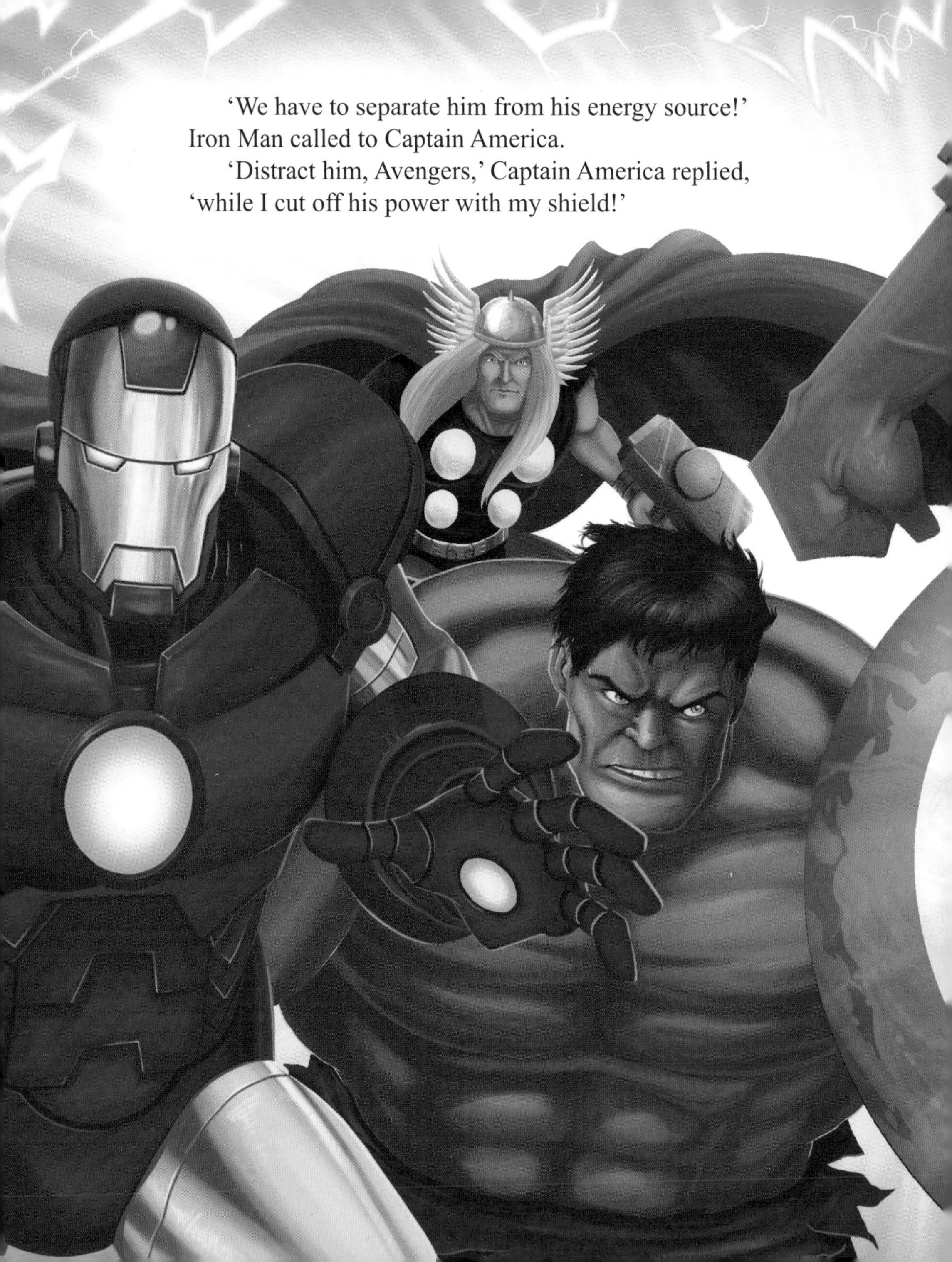

'We have to separate him from his energy source!' Iron Man called to Captain America.

'Distract him, Avengers,' Captain America replied, 'while I cut off his power with my shield!'

The Avengers attacked Zzzax. The monster swatted at them, but the heroes were too strong and too fast.

'Keep him busy, Avengers!' Iron Man shouted. 'Now, Cap!'

Captain America threw his mighty shield. It sliced through the arcs of electricity, interrupting the flow of power to the monster.

With his power cut off, Zzzax began to get smaller. 'Hulk stop Zzzax!' the green giant roared as he cracked open a nearby fire hydrant. 'Hulk SPLASH!'

Water from the hydrant hit the monster, causing him to spark and short-circuit. Zzzax's energy began to drain away. 'Zzzax is all washed up!' Captain America said.

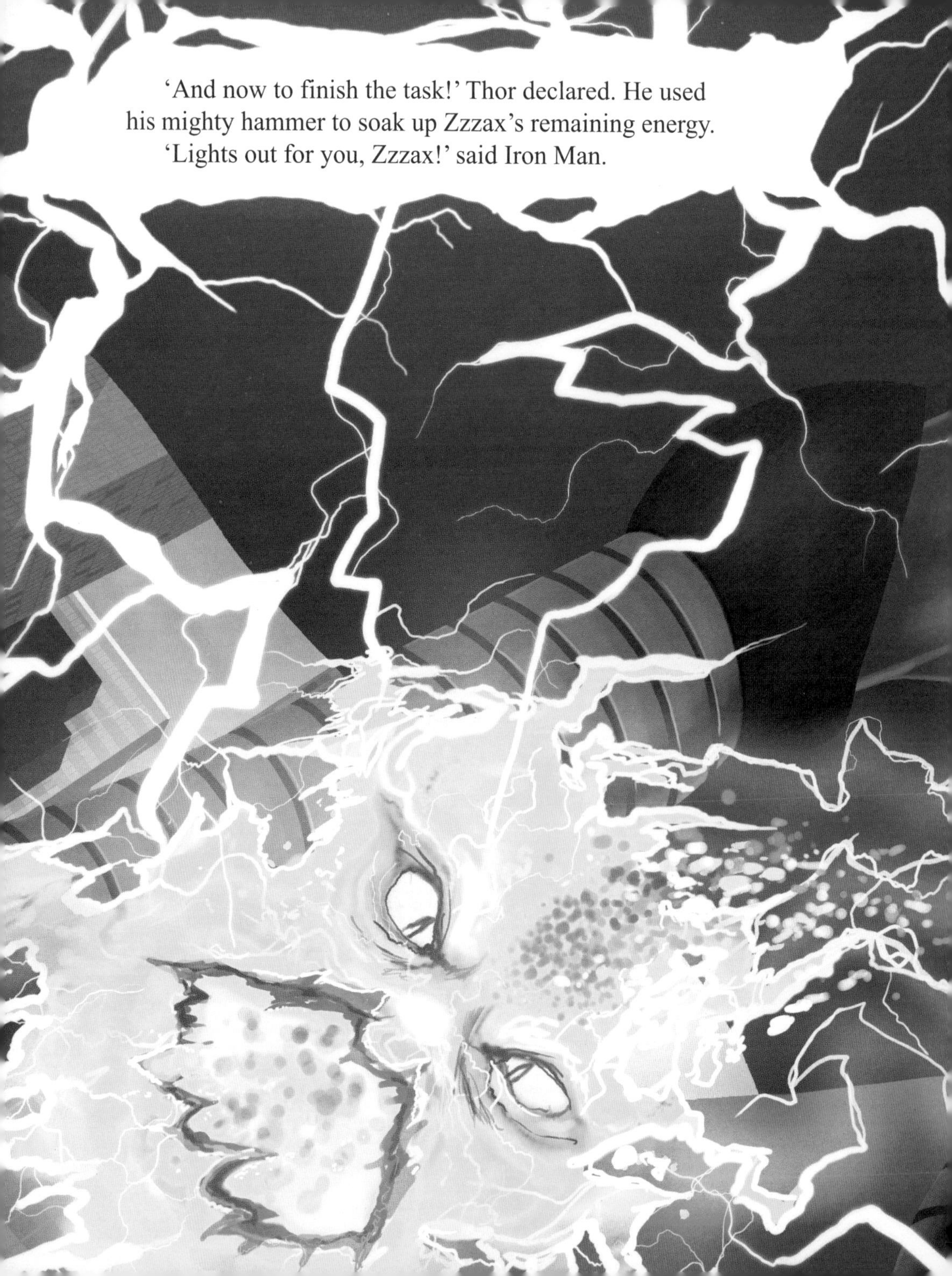

'And now to finish the task!' Thor declared. He used his mighty hammer to soak up Zzzax's remaining energy.

'Lights out for you, Zzzax!' said Iron Man.

Then Thor held the hammer high above his head.

'Power, back from whence you came!' he thundered, releasing the energy. The city lit up once more!

'The lights are on again in the city that never sleeps,' said Captain America.

'Hulk like sleep,' the green giant rumbled.

'Not now, Hulk. We've got a power plant to rebuild,' Iron Man said. 'Come on, Avengers.'

AVENGERS ASSEMBLE!

Treasure Cove Stories

Please contact Centum Books to receive the full list of titles in the *Treasure Cove Stories* series. books@centumbooksltd.co.uk

1 Three Little Pigs
2 Snow White and the Seven Dwarfs
3 The Fox and the Hound - Hide-and-Seek
4 Dumbo
5 Cinderella
6 Cinderella's Friends
7 Alice in Wonderland
8 Mad Hatter's Tea Party from Alice in Wonderland
9 Mickey Mouse and his Spaceship
10 Peter Pan
11 Pinocchio
12 Mickey and the Beanstalk
13 Sleeping Beauty and the Good Fairies
14 The Lucky Puppy
15 Chicken Little
16 The Incredibles
17 Coco
18 Winnie the Pooh and Tigger
19 The Sword in the Stone
20 Mary Poppins
21 The Jungle Book
22 Aristocats
23 Lady and the Tramp
24 Bambi
25 Bambi - Friends of the Forest
26 Pete's Dragon
27 Beauty and the Beast - The Teapot's Tale
28 Monsters, Inc. – M is for Monster
29 Finding Nemo
30 The Incredibles 2
31 The Incredibles – Jack-Jack Attack
33 Wall-E
34 Up
35 The Princess and the Frog
36 Toy Story – The Pet Problem
39 Spider-Man – Night of the Vulture!
40 Wreck it Ralph
41 Ralph Breaks the Internet
42 The Invincible Iron Man - Eye of the Dragon
45 Toy Story – A Roaring Adventure
46 Cars – Deputy Mater Saves the Day!
47 Spider-Man – Trapped by the Green Goblin
49 Spider-Man – High Voltage!
50 Frozen
51 Cinderella is my Babysitter
52 Beauty and the Beast - I am the Beast
56 I am a Princess
57 The Big Book of Paw Patrol
58 Paw Patrol - Adventures with Grandpa!
59 Paw Patrol - Pirate Pups!
60 Trolls
61 Trolls Holiday
63 Zootropolis
64 Ariel is my Babysitter
65 Tiana is my Babysitter
66 Belle is my Babysitter
67 Paw Patrol - Itty-Bitty Kitty Rescue
68 Moana
70 Guardians of the Galaxy
71 Captain America - High-Stakes Heist!
72 Ant-Man
73 The Mighty Avengers
74 The Mighty Avengers - Lights Out!
75 The Incredible Hulk
78 Paw Patrol - All-Star Pups!
80 I am Ariel
82 Jasmine is my Babysitter
87 Beauty and the Beast - I am Belle
88 The Lion Guard - The Imaginary Okapi
89 Thor - Thunder Strike!
90 Guardians of the Galaxy - Rocket to the Rescue!
93 Olaf's Frozen Adventure
95 Trolls - Branch's Bunker Birthday
96 Trolls - Poppy's Party
97 The Ugly Duckling
98 Cars - Look Out for Mater!
99 101 Dalmatians
100 The Sorcerer's Apprentice
101 Tangled
102 Avengers – The Threat of Thanos
105 The Mighty Thor
106 Doctor Strange
107 Captain Marvel
108 The Invincible Iron Man
110 The Big Freeze
111 Ratatouille
112 Aladdin
113 Aladdin - I am the Genie
114 Seven Dwarfs Find a House
115 Toy Story
116 Toy Story 4
117 Paw Patrol - Jurassic Bark!
118 Paw Patrol - Mighty Pup Power!
121 The Lion King - I am Simba
122 Winnie the Pooh - The Honey Tree
123 Frozen II
124 Baby Shark and the Colours of the Ocean
125 Baby Shark and the Police Sharks!
126 Trolls World Tour
127 I am Elsa
128 I am Anna
129 I am Olaf
130 I am Mulan
131 Sleeping Beauty
132 Onward
133 Paw Patrol – Puppy Birthday to You!
134 Black Widow
135 Trolls – Poppy's Big Day!
136 Baby Shark and the Tooth Fairy
137 Baby Shark – Mummy Shark
138 Inside Out
139 The Prince and the Pauper
140 Finding Dory
142 The Lion King - Simba's Daring Rescue

•Book list may be subject to change. Not all titles are listed.

TCS
TCS